Y0-CBS-346

Your Lie in April

*I met the girl
under full-bloomed cherry blossoms,
and my fate has begun to change.*

1

Naoshi Arakawa

contents

Your Lie in April

I met the girl under full-bloomed cherry blossoms, and my fate has begun to change.

Chapter 1: Monotone

al **Piano Comp**

Sponsored by Maihō Shimbun

...I...

...HAVEN'T BEEN ABLE TO PLAY THE PIANO.

WE AIN'T LOVE-BIRDS!!

WINCE

TAKE YOUR FILTHY SHOES OFF!

AREN'T YOU IN THE MIDDLE OF SOCCER PRACTICE?

WHAT ARE YOU DOING WITH YOUR PHONE?

STUPID VICE PRINCIPAL BALDY.

SLAPPING KIDS IN THE FACE OVER A LITTLE BROKEN GLASS.

IT'S STANDING RIGHT WHERE ALL THE BALLS ARE GONNA GO.

I LIKE IT. ALL THE GIRLS CAN WATCH FROM THE WINDOWS AND CHEER FOR ME.

AND *I'M* THE ONE GETTING SLAPPED.

FOR ONE THING...

...THAT BUILDING IS IN THE STUPIDEST LOCATION.

NICE GUYS...

...ALWAYS FINISH LAST.

SMIRK

BUT KŌSEI, YOU'D BETTER REIN IT IN.

WHOA!

I GOT A TEXT FROM KEIKO-CHAN!!

♪

!

THREE.

HOW MANY IS THAT NOW?

ZOOM

MR. SUPER-FICIAL.

I HAVE NO IDEA WHAT THEY SEE IN HIM.

I GOTTA GO!!

"THE MOMENT I MET HIM...

...MY WHOLE LIFE CHANGED."

MIWA WAS SAYING...

EVERYTHING AROUND ME...

...STARTED TO FILL WITH GLORIOUS COLOR."

...EVERYTHING I FELT.

"EVERYTHING I SAW, EVERYTHING I HEARD...

3 - 3

...TO ME...

BUT...

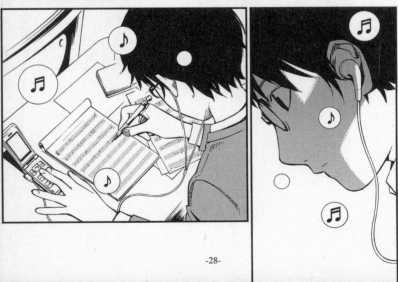

WE'RE MEETING UP TOMORROW.

THERE'S A GIRL IN MY CLASS.

SHE WANTED ME TO INTRODUCE HER TO WATARI.

SO... YOU HAVE PLANS?

...

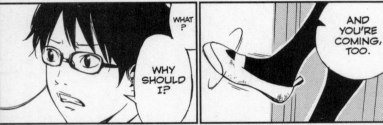

WHAT?

WHY SHOULD I?

AND YOU'RE COMING, TOO.

AND SHE PLAYS THE VIOLIN.

IF IT'S JUST ME AND HER AND WATARI...

...IT'S GONNA BE AWKWARD FOR ME.

IF IT'S GONNA BE ALL SAPPY SWEET ANYWAY...

...THEN TWO AND TWO IS MUCH BETTER.

I'M HOME.

PIANO PRODIGY KOSEI ARIMA, AGE 9

YOUNGEST WINNER IN HISTORY

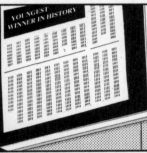

AWARD

TAKAHATA PIANO COMPETITION

FIRST PRIZE

MOM,
I'M
HOME.

OH YEAH,
IT'S THE
SAME DAY
OF THE
MONTH AS
THE DAY
YOU DIED.

...PIANO.

PROBABLY BECAUSE I HAVE NOTHING ELSE.

AND YET I STILL CLING TO IT.

TAKE THE PIANO FROM ME...

...AND I'M EMPTY.

THERE'S NOTHING LEFT BUT THE LINGERING STRAINS OF A CLUMSILY PLAYED LAST NOTE.

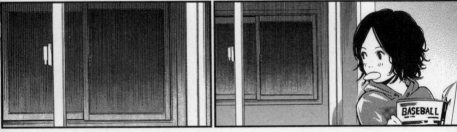

NO
PIANO
FROM
NEXT
DOOR
TODAY,
EITHER.

...

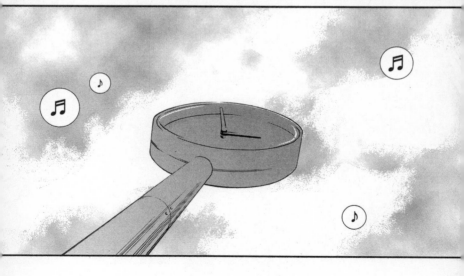

"EVERY-THING I SAW...

...EVERY-THING I HEARD...

...EVERY-THING I FELT.

EVERY-THING...

...STARTED TO FILL WITH GLORIOUS COLOR."

...AROUND ME...

TEARS.

COUGH

I BLEW TOO HARD...

COUGH

ONE-CHAN!

THE DOVES AREN'T COMING.

THEY LOOK JUST LIKE A PAINTING.

...

AHRM

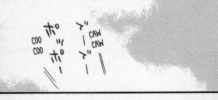

COO
COO

NICE TO MEET YOU.

GLINT

AND.

SPARKLE

PLEASED TO MEET YOU.

NICE JOB, TSUBAKI.

SHE'S SO CUTE...

BELIEVE IT OR NOT, HE'S CAPTAIN OF THE SOCCER TEAM.

THIS IS RYŌTA WATARI.

SULK

NUMBER 23

...BUT THIS IS OUR FOURTH WHEEL, "FRIEND A."

AND, NOT THAT ANYBODY CARES...

OH, STOP. TEE HEE HEE.

I ALMOST GAVE IN TO HER CHARMS. HOW EMBARRASSING.

TALK ABOUT YOUR ONE-EIGHTY.

WINCE

PLEASE EXCUSE MY BE-HAVIOR BEFORE.

SOOO CUTE!

OH!

RUMBLE

RUMBLE

RUMBLE

RUMBLE

SHE'S SO POLITE.

BEAM

SO THIS IS THE FACE OF HELL...

SAY ONE WORD, AND I KILL YOU.

PEEPING TOM.

I'D BETTER KEEP AN EYE ON YOU, HUH?

HERE YOU ARE, TALKING TO HER, TRYING TO GET TO HER FIRST.

!

C'MERE, KŌSEI.

TOWA HALL

...BE-
GAN
TO
RUN
...

...ON
MY
OWN
TWO
FEET.

Monotone...The End

Your Lie in April

I met the girl under full-bloomed cherry blossoms, and my fate has begun to change.

Your Lie in April

I met the girl under full-bloomed cherry blossoms, and my fate has begun to change.

WHAT TIME IS THE COMPETITION?

AND THE COMPETITION IS AT THREE-THIRTY.

LET'S SEE, THE HALL OPENS AT THREE.

ERK!

IT'S PRACTICALLY STARTING!

IT'S THREE-TWENTY NOW!

Chapter 2: The Love of a Violinist

-74-

I'M THIS WAY.

WELL...

A DIFFERENT WORLD...

EVERYONE'S SO HIGH-CLASS.

YOU CAN DO IT.

WE'LL BE HERE CHEERING YOU ON.

AUDIENCE SEATING IS THIS WAY.

Tōwa Music Competition

KAZAMA-SENSEI IS THE HEAD JUDGE!

THIS IS HER CHANCE TO GET HIS ATTENTION.

I'LL GO CHECK ON HER.

I HOPE HE DOES A GOOD JOB.

WAIT, IS THAT...?

IT'S ARIMA.

ARIMA-KUN!!

THERE ARE SEATS OVER THERE.

...WHEN I CAME HERE TO WATCH KŌSEI.

I HAVEN'T BEEN IN A PLACE LIKE THIS SINCE SIXTH GRADE...

HE'S SO GROWN UP.

ARIMA?

THE PIANIST?

I THOUGHT HE WENT OVERSEAS.

WHAT'S HE DOING AT A VIOLIN COMPETITION?

THE YOUNGEST TO WIN THE SAIKI COMPETITION?

I GUESS CLASSICAL MUSIC IS A SMALL WORLD.

ブスー

SULK

WHAP

ビリ

HA! MR. EX-CELEBRITY!

WE WILL NOW BEGIN THE COMPETI-TION.

CLAP

CLAP

1

THE "KREUTZER."

BEETHOVEN'S VIOLIN SONATA NUMBER 9.

...IN A LONG TIME.

I HAVEN'T HEARD A LIVE PERFORMANCE...

HE'S ASLEEP ALREADY?!

WELL, IT'S A FAIRLY NEW COMPETITION, AND IT'S NATIONAL.

IT'S GETTING SOME ATTENTION.

THE WINNER GETS THE PRIVILEGE OF PERFORMING A RECITAL...

...USING THE SPONSOR'S OWN GUARNERI.*

THE SPONSOR IS DOING THINGS A LITTLE DIFFERENTLY.

TOWA HALL

USUALLY, THEY ASSIGN AN UNACCOMPANIED PIECE FOR THE PRELIMINARIES, LIKE BACH OR PAGANINI.

BUT FOR THIS COMPETITION, EVERYONE NEEDS PIANO ACCOMPANIMENT.

THAT'S NOT REALLY NORMAL.

COOL.

GARNERY?

PAGANINI?

GRIN   GRIN

*GUARNERI: A FAMOUS MAKE OF VIOLIN, ON PAR WITH STRADIVARIUS.

CLAP
CLAP

CLAP

③
Public

THAT'S
TOO
BAD.

HE
STARTED
OUT SO
WELL.

HE WAS PANICKING.

HIS BOWING GOT PRETTY ROUGH IN THE MIDDLE THERE.

THAT EXPLAINS IT.

THERE WERE TWO OR THREE PLACES WHERE HE SLIPPED.

AND THAT'S ONE OF SATŌ-SENSEI'S STUDENTS?

THEY'RE ALL GIVING STEADY PERFORMANCES.

TILT TILT

THEY'RE ROUGH AROUND THE EDGES, BUT THEY'RE ALL PLAYING AT A HIGH LEVEL.

STILL, WE HAVE A FINE CROP OF MUSICIANS HERE.

HEAD JUDGE

IF THIS KEEPS UP, I'M GONNA FALL ASLEEP.

LET'S SEE, NEXT WE HAVE...

OF COURSE, IT DIDN'T GET INTERESTING UNTIL HE MESSED UP.

YOU'RE ABSOLUTELY RIGHT, KAZAMA-SENSEI.

WILL MY MUSIC...

...GET THROUGH TO THEM?

FRUGATIVI ET APPELAVI.

ELOHIM ESSAIM. ELOHIM ESSAIM.

SHE'S
SO
CUTE!

SHE'S PLAYING IT ALL HER OWN WAY...

...AND IGNORING HER ACCOMPANIST.

THE TEMPO AND... ...THE DYNAMICS ARE WAY OFF.

SCRITCH

SCRITCH

...

DOES SHE HAVE NO INTENTION OF PLAYING AS INSTRUCTED ?!

IN A COMPETITION, FAITHFULNESS TO THE SCORE IS VITAL.

IT IS THE "KREUTZER"!... BUT...

...THIS MUSIC IS NOT BEETHOVEN'S.

IT'S AS IF SHE'S PICKING A FIGHT WITH THE COMPOSER.

WAAA

WELL.

WELL.

WELL.

NOW THAT WAS SOMETHING.

SHE DOESN'T BLINDLY FOLLOW THE SCORE.

SHE HAS OVERWHELMING INDIVIDUALITY.

KAORI-CHAN, YOU'RE THE BEST!

SQUEE

AHEM! THIS IS A SERIOUS CONTEST!

SHE'S A JAPANESE NADJA!

BRAVO!

AAAH

IT'S LIKE WE'RE AT A POP CONCERT!

AAAH

WOW.

THE CROWD'S STILL BUZZING.

NO, SHE'S NOT GOING TO WIN. SHE WON'T EVEN PLACE.

SHE DID TOO MANY THINGS WRONG.

THE ONE THING YOU NEVER WANT TO DO IN A COMPETI- TION IS IGNORE THE SHEET MUSIC.

YOU THINK SHE'LL WIN?

HUH?

OH.

...THAT'S NOT WHAT SHE WAS AFTER ANYWAY...

IT WOULD BE ONE THING IF THIS WERE A RECITAL, BUT YOU CAN'T DO THAT IN A COMPETI- TION.

BUT... I'M PRETTY SURE...

AWW, WHY?

EVERY- BODY LOVED IT.

IS THAT ALLOWED?

NUMBER FOUR WAS AMAZING, RIGHT?

AND NOW FOR A FIFTEEN-MINUTE INTERMISSION.

KAORI MIYAZONO, RIGHT?

I'M GONNA REMEMBER HER.

SHE REALLY BLEW EVERYONE AWAY.

I'M HER NEWEST FAN.

SHE'S SO CUTE.

SHE WAS SO COOL UP THERE.

EVERYBODY'S TALKING ABOUT KAO-CHAN.

IT REALLY WAS LIKE WE CAME TO A ROCK CONCERT INSTEAD.

WOW.

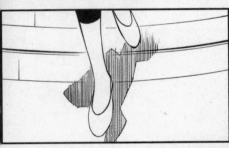

KAO-CHAAN!

I KNOW.

FRIEND A.

YOU'RE JUST A SUPPORT-ING ROLE.

KAO-CHAN LIKES WATARI.

-116-

AFTER HER PER-FOR-MANCE...

...THE VIOLIN-IST...

...RUNS OVER TO THE MAN WAITING FOR HER.

SHE WEAVES HER WAY THROUGH THE CROWD...

...HER FLOWERS IN HER ARMS.

...HER EYES FIXED ON HER TARGET.

JUST LIKE A SCENE FROM A MOVIE.

THANK YOU.

YOU WERE SUPER CUTE UP THERE.

AH HA HA.

NO WAY.

YOU'RE TOTALLY GONNA WIN, KAORI-CHAN.

ite: Miyazono, Kaor

YOUR LIE IN APRIL FEATURED MUSIC

BEETHOVEN'S VIOLIN SONATA NO.9:
THE KREUTZER SONATA,
FIRST MOVEMENT

Of Beethoven's ten violin sonatas (compositions for violin and piano), this and his fifth, "Spring," are the most famous. Consisting of three movements, it is a long piece that, in full, lasts nearly half an hour.

"Kreutzer" is the name of the violinist to whom the piece was dedicated. However, due to various circumstances, the piece was never performed by Kreutzer himself.

The words "violin sonata" tend to give the impression that the piece features the violin while the piano is mere accompaniment, but in this piece, the two instruments are more equal. One might call it more of a double concerto. A high level of skill is required for both the piano and the violin, and the piece demands intense concentration and stamina.

Nevertheless, the sense of exhilaration that comes after playing it to the end is one that cannot be matched.

(Violinist Rieko Ikeda)

Watch it on Youtube
(Search for "Kodansha *Your Lie in April* Featured Music")

Music Room

Chapter 3: Black Cat

THAT'S WHY...

...LOVE IS SO UNFAIR.

BUT...

...

I CAN'T BE LIKE THAT.

NOT ME.

YEAH.

I'M IN LOVE WITH A LOT OF GIRLS.

I THINK I CAN SEE WHY SO MANY GIRLS LIKE YOU, WATARI.

...WHAT MY MOTHER LEFT IN MY HEART...

I WANT TO HEAR IT AGAIN.

BUT I DON'T WANT TO.

I WANT...

...SEEMS TO SCATTER AWAY.

AND EVERY TIME IT DOES...

...TO SEE HER AGAIN.

...BUT I DON'T WANT TO.

SHE REALLY DOES GO TO OUR SCHOOL.

SHE'S WEARING OUR SCHOOL UNIFORM.

STARE STARE STARE STARE STARE

WH—

SWEAT

WHY ARE YOU STARING AT ME?

HEH HEH

POST IT IF YOU MUST.

IT WILL ONLY STOKE THE FIRES OF MY POPULARITY.

FULL OF HERSELF.

I'M NOT GOING TO AND I DIDN'T!!

PERVERT!

I JUST KNOW YOU'VE GOT A DIRTY BLOG.

THAT'S A LIE!

I SEE THE DIRTY LOOK IN YOUR EYES!

YOU'RE GOING TO TAKE NAUGHTY PICTURES OF ME AGAIN!

I'M WAITING HERE TO AMBUSH HIM.

I WANTED TO SURPRISE HIM.

WATARI?

ANYWAY, WHERE'S WATARI-KUN?

YOU'RE A JERK.

I HAVEN'T SEEN HER IN A WHILE.

I THINK I'LL SKIP PRACTICE AND GO HOME WITH KEIKO-CHAN TODAY.

WATARI IS...

...STILL AT PRACTICE.

HOW MUCH LONGER?

HERE YOU ARE. ONE FRESH WAFFLE WITH STRAWBERRY SAUCE.

IT'S BLINDING ME!

OOOH...

IT'S DAZZLING!

SHE'S SERIOUS ABOUT WAFFLES.

SPARKLE SPARKLE

OOOOHH

BEAM

I'VE ALWAYS WANTED TO TRY ONE.

I'VE BEEN MEANING TO CHECK OUT THIS CAFE.

FIRST I'M AN EXTRA, NOW I'M AN UNDER-STUDY.

IS THAT WHY YOU WERE WAIT-ING FOR WATARI?

THE WAFFLES IN THE PICTURES LOOK SO GOOD.

I'M SICK OF BA-NANAS.

PLAYING THE VIOLIN TAKES A LOT OF STAMINA.

IT IS ES-SENTIAL THAT I GET ENOUGH SUGAR TO SUSTAIN MY ENERGY LEVELS.

WE'RE NOT SUP-POSED TO BUY FOOD IN OUR SCHOOL UNIFORMS.

SOUNDS LIKE AN EXCUSE.

SMACK

I KNOW THAT!

SO YOU DO KNOW THE RULES!

I'M IN HEAVEN...

YUM-MMM-MM!

SHE'S SUCH A BRILLIANT PER-FORMER.

BUT IT'S IMPOSSIBLE TO SEE HER AS ANYTHING BUT A NORMAL GIRL.

HEY!!

GIVE ME YOURS, TOO!

THAT'S MY WAFFLE !!

SEE?
I
KNEW
IT.

IT IS A
HAPPY
PIANO.

HO!

YOU HAVE SAND IN YOUR HAIR...

MEOW!

MEOW!

WHOA?!

ROLL

KIT-TY!

MEOW!

ROLL

ROLL

IT
CAN
HAPPEN
TO
ANYONE,
RIGHT?

...TWIST
TOGETHER
LIKE
FLOWERS
CARRIED
OFF...

...BY A
SPRING
GALE.

THEY
FLY
AWAY...

...AND
VANISH.

YEAH.

THAT MIGHT BE TRUE FOR YOU.

WHEN I'M WITH YOU...

...I THINK I UNDER-STAND...

...WHAT WATARI WAS SAYING.

IT'S THAT LOVE THAT MAKES HER SHINE BRIGHT-ER.

YOU FALL IN LOVE WITH THE VIOLIN.

YOU FALL IN LOVE WITH FOOD.

YOU FALL IN LOVE WITH THE LITTLE THINGS THAT HAPPEN EVERY DAY.

YOU FALL IN LOVE WITH MUSIC.

WHAT SHOULD I CALL THIS FEELING?

MAYBE THAT'S WHY YOU...

I THINK...

...SHINE SO BRIGHTLY.

Your Lie in April

I met the girl under full-bloomed cherry blossoms, and my fate has begun to change.

YOUR LIE IN APRIL FEATURED MUSIC

MOZART
VARIATIONS ON
"TWINKLE, TWINKLE, LITTLE STAR"

A piano piece consisting of twelve variations of
a contemporary French folk melody that Mozart
composed for the education of students.

In the manga, the children are playing the
main melody (the one you're all familiar with:
"Twinkle, Twinkle, Little Star"), and Kōsei
plays the first of the twelve variations over it.

It may sound simple at first listen, but that's
Mozart for you. Anyone who hears it will be
amazed at what can be done with the melody,
and that surprise and pleasure will fill the
listener with joy.

Incidentally, the translation of the original title
is, "Ah, Mother, If I Could Tell You."

(Violinist Rieko Ikeda)

Watch it on Youtube.
Search "Kodansha *Your Lie in April* featured music"

Chapter 4: Colorful

THAT'S AN UNUSUAL CHOICE.

THEY USUALLY PLAY SOME KIND OF POP MUSIC.

SAINT-SAËNS, INTRODUCTION AND RONDO CAPRICCIOSO...

RAT-TLE

AND IT'S ON REPEAT.

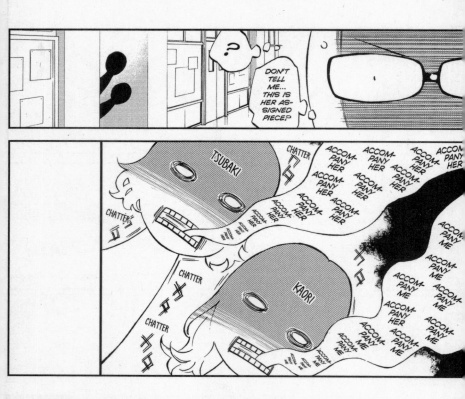

BUT THAT'S WEIRD FOR THE COMPETITION TO BE ON A WEEKDAY.

TOMORROW'S THE DAY.

YOU THINK IT'LL STOP RAINING?

WOW, THAT'S COOL.

"CHILDREN NEED THEIR DAYS OFF."

THAT'S THE SPONSOR'S POLICY.

BUT I GUESS THEY HAD TO HAVE THE PRELIMINARIES ON A SATURDAY BECAUSE THERE WERE SO MANY CONTESTANTS.

BUT...

...WAS IT REALLY A GOOD IDEA?

FORCING HIM TO ACCOMPANY ME.

...SO WE'LL BRING HIM ALONG BY FORCE.

WE CAN BE PRETTY SURE KŌSEI'S GONNA FLAKE OUT ON YOU.

...

GOOD IDEA!

IT WAS A GOOD!

IDEA!

OH, IT'S FINE.

IF YOU WANT KŌSEI TO DO ANYTHING, YOU HAVE TO PUSH HIM AT LEAST THIS HARD.

HE COULD NEVER SAY NO TO A GIR— ER, TO YOU, KAO-CHAN.

OH, WE CAN GET WATARI TO HELP, TOO.

THAT'S ...

... NOT IT, EXACTLY.

HMMM.

I'M AN ONLY CHILD.

BUT I FEEL LIKE I'VE ALWAYS HAD A BIG SISTER TO TAKE CARE OF.

TO ME, KŌSEI...

...IS LIKE MY HOPELESS LITTLE BROTHER.

TO BE HONEST...

...

...KŌSEI CAN PLAY THE PIANO OR NOT.

I COULDN'T CARE LESS EITHER WAY.

WHAT?

TIME REALLY CAN STOP.

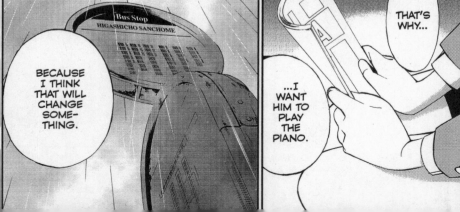

BECAUSE I THINK THAT WILL CHANGE SOMETHING.

THAT'S WHY...

...I WANT HIM TO PLAY THE PIANO.

NEXT STOP, TOTSUHARA UNIVERSITY HOSPITAL.

TOTSUHARA UNIVERSITY HOSPITAL.

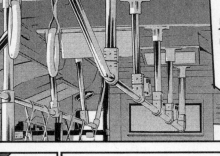

STOP REQUESTED

PLEASE PUSH THIS BUTTON TO REQUE A ST

DING

TŌWA MUSIC COMPETITION

TOWA HALL

1

BEEP

...THE SECOND ROUND FOR OUR VIOLIN DIVISION.

WE WILL NOW BEGIN...

TILT TILT

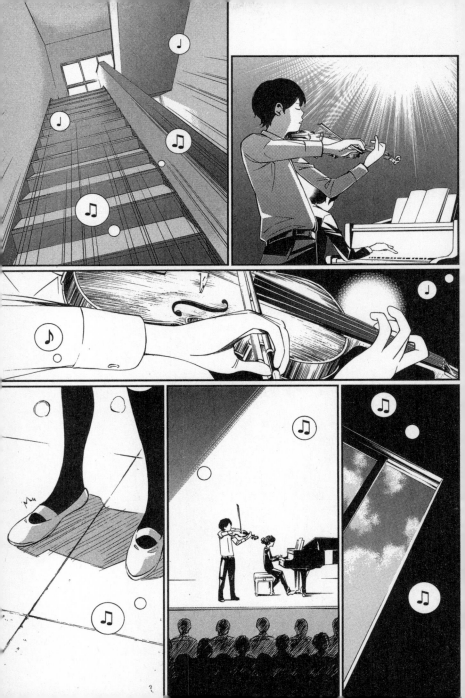

BABONG

KICK

GYAAAH!

WHAT DO YOU THINK YOU'RE DOING?!!!

I LOOKED EVERY-WHERE!

NOW LET'S GET GOING!!

WHIP

I CAME TO GET YOU, AND YOU KNOW IT!!

HIDING OUT HERE!

FSHH

BESIDES, EVEN IF I DID...

...I'D DO AN AWFUL JOB.

I CAN'T ACCOMPANY YOU.

THERE ARE PEOPLE STUDYING JUST TO BE ACCOMPANISTS.

I TOLD YOU FROM THE BEGINNING!

I'M NOT GONNA DO IT!!

WHAT?!

...

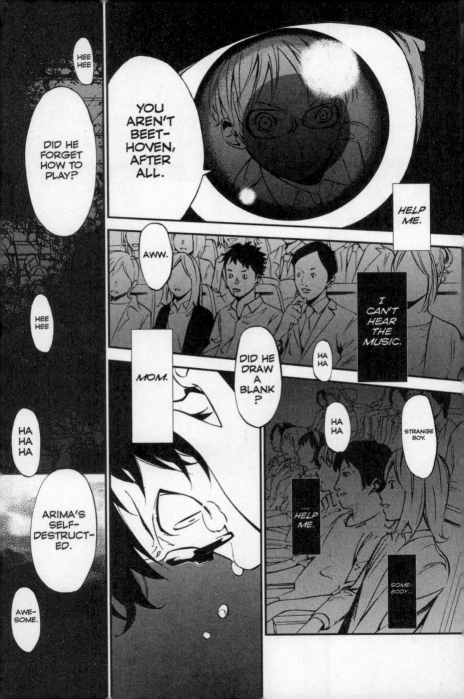

SO THAT I CAN LIVE FOREVER IN THEIR HEARTS.

...WILL ALWAYS REMEMBER ME.

SO THAT THE PEOPLE KIND ENOUGH TO LISTEN...

BECAUSE I'M A MUSICIAN.

SO...

JUST LIKE YOU.

...PLEASE.

THAT IS MY REASON FOR BEING.

Special Thanks:

AKINORI ŌSAWA

RIEKO IKEDA

KAORI YAMAZAKI

YOSHIHIRO KAMIYA

TOPPAN HALL

KAWAGUCHI LILIA

MUSIC HALL ANOANO

Translation Notes

Melodica, page 46

As you can see in the picture, a melodica (known in Japan as a pianica) is keyboard instrument that the musician blows into. It sounds something like a harmonica, and is popular in musical education. That being the case, it's something you might expect to be played by a someone in grade school, and not a serious musician.

Pazu, page 52

Pazu is one of the main characters in the Studio Ghibli film, *Castle in the Sky*. Apparently the children are trying to replicate the scene where Pazu plays his trumpet while his pet doves fly around. Kōsei sees doves flying during the girl's solo, so it's possible that the children's complaint is referring to the end of the solo, when the doves are supposed gather back around the musician. Either that, or Kōsei is so moved by the music that he sees doves that aren't really there. Incidentally, in Japanese, the same word is used for dove and for pigeon, which is just as well, because doves and pigeons are in the same family of birds.

Kaori's pre-performance chant, page 94

This is a chant from the Red Dragon Grimoire, which contains spells for summoning demons. This particular incantation was famous enough to be used in manga series such as *Akuma-kun*, which is most likely where Kaori first read it. The first part is never translated into Japanese, which makes it difficult for Japanese-English translators to translate into English, but the second half means, roughly, "I seek and beseech thee."

The Japanese Nadja, page 109

This is a reference to the famous American violinist, Nadja Salerno-Sonnenberg, who is known for her wild, original playing.

Her Majesty is satisfied, page 155

In the Japanese version, Kaori uses the word *yo* for "I." This is a rather pompous first-person pronoun, and so the translators have decided to translate it as "Her Majesty."

Beethoven and Mozart, page 166

Kaori's suggestions to help a pianist play despite difficulties come from historical anecdotes. One of the methods Beethoven used to help him through his hearing loss was to put a ruler in his mouth and touch it to his piano so he could feel the sound vibrations in his head even if he couldn't hear them. Mozart was a student of Haydn, who bet his students that no one could compose a piece of music he (Haydn) couldn't play on sight. Mozart took him up on this bet and wrote a simple piano piece that at one point required the musician to have a hand on each of the far ends of the keyboard, and at the same time play a note in the middle of the keyboard. When Haydn declared that no one could play such a piece, Mozart proved him wrong by using his long nose to play the middle note.

Your Lie in April volume 1 is a work of fiction. Names, characters, places, and incidents are the products of the author's imagination or are used fictitiously. Any resemblance to actual events, locales, or persons, living or dead, is entirely coincidental.

A Kodansha Comics Trade Paperback Original
Your Lie in April volume 1 copyright © 2011 Naoshi Arakawa
English translation copyright © 2015 Naoshi Arakawa

All rights reserved.

Published in the United States by Kodansha Comics, an imprint of Kodansha USA Publishing, LLC, New York.

Publication rights for this English edition arranged through Kodansha Ltd, Tokyo.

ISBN 978-1-63236-325-1

Special thanks:
Akinori Osawa, Rieko Ikeda, and Kaori Yamazaki

Printed in the United States of America.

www.kodanshacomics.com

9 8 7 6 5 4 3 2 1
Translation: Alethea and Athena Nibley
Lettering: Scott Brown
Editing: Ben Applegate

Kodansha Comics edition cover design by Phil Balsman